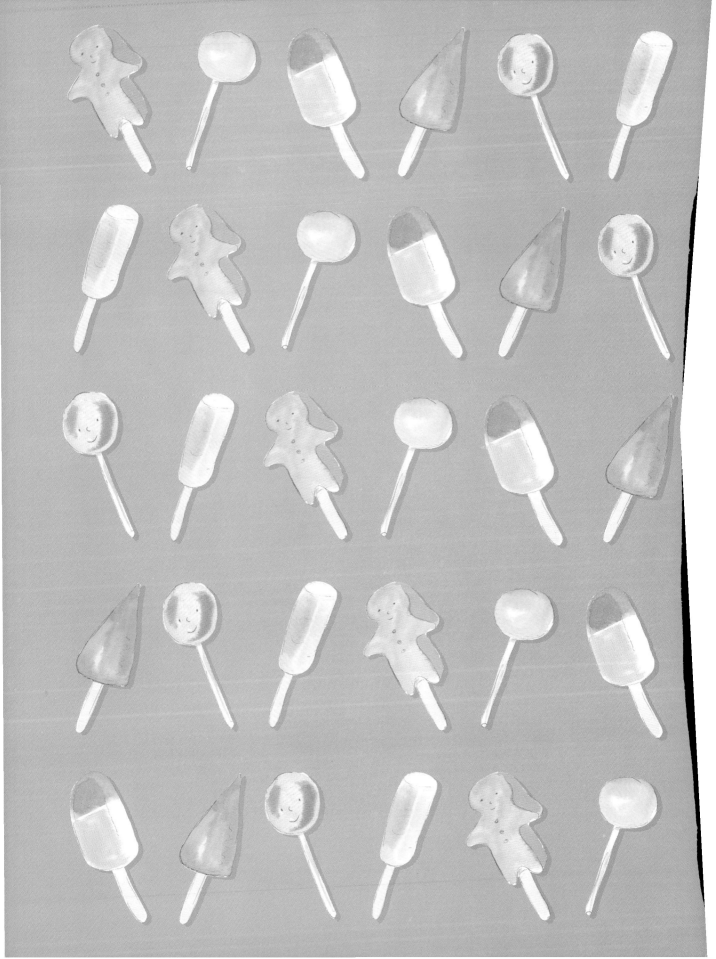

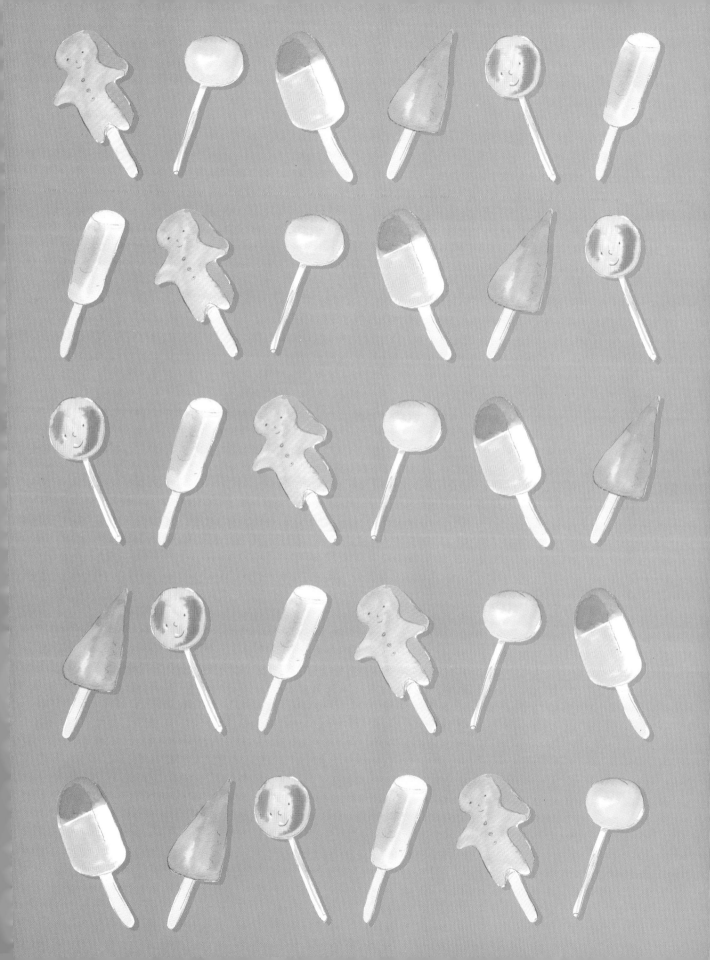

Lollipops

Bouncing
Ben

and other rhymes

Original poems by **John Foster**

Illustrated by **John Wallace**

Oxford University Press

Oxford University Press, Great Clarendon Street, Oxford OX2 6DP

Oxford New York
Athens Auckland Bangkok Bogota Bombay
Buenos Aires Calcutta Cape Town Dar es Salaam Delhi
Florence Hong Kong Istanbul Karachi
Kuala Lumpur Madras Madrid Melbourne
Mexico City Nairobi Paris Singapore
Taipei Tokyo Toronto Warsaw

and associated companies in
Berlin Ibadan

Oxford is a trade mark of Oxford University Press

Text copyright © John Foster 1998
Illustrations copyright © John Wallace 1998
First published 1998

A CIP catalogue record for this book is available
from the British Library

ISBN 0 19 276181 1

Printed in Belgium

Contents

Bouncing Ben

Bouncing Ben bouncing on the bed,
Bounced to the ceiling and banged his head.

Bouncing Ben landed on the floor.
Bouncing Ben with his bottom sore.

Bouncing Ben lying on his bed,
A bump on his bottom and a lump on his head.

boing

Stretching, stretching

Stretching, stretching, stretching high.
Stretch up till you touch the sky.

Crouching, crouching, crouching small.
Curl into a tiny ball.

Whirling, whirling, whirling round.
Fall down dizzy on the ground.

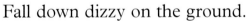

When Susie's eating custard

When Susie's eating custard,
It splashes everywhere.
Down her bib, up her nose,
All over her high chair.

She pokes it with her fingers.
She spreads it on her hair.
When Susie's eating custard,
She gets it everywhere.

10

One for the pineapple

One for the pineapple for our tea.
Two for the plums in the old plum tree.
Three for the empty banana skins.
Four for the peach juice on our chins.
Five for a bunch of bright red cherries.
Six for a handful of ripe blackberries.
Seven for the apples in the pie Dad made.
Eight for the lemons in the lemonade.
Nine for the oranges we squeezed for squash.
Ten for the fingers that need a wash.

With my hand

With my hand
I can turn on a tap.
With my hand
I can give you a clap.

With my hand
I can scratch my nose.
With my hand
I can tickle my toes.

With my hand
I can scoop up sand.
With my hand
I can hold your hand.

With my hand
I can squeeze very tight.
With my hand
I can switch off the light.

With my hand
I can point to the sky.
With my hand
I can wave goodbye!

I am the boss

I am the boss
What I say goes.
Clap your hands
And touch your toes.

I am the boss.
Look over here.
Waggle your thumbs
And scratch your ear.

I am the boss.
Eat up your egg.
Wave your arms
And shake your leg.

I am the boss.
Jump like a clown.
Bend your knees
And sit down!

I am the boss.
Nod your head.
Close your eyes
And go up to bed.

You can't catch me!

I chased Tina.
Tina chased Lee.
Lee chased Pat.
Pat chased me.

   In and out the bushes.
   Round and round the tree.
   Up and down the garden.
   You can't catch me!

I chased Pat.
Pat chased Lee.
Lee chased Tina.
Tina chased me.

Locked out again

One, two, three,
Mum's lost her key.

Four, five, six,
We're in a fix.

Seven, eight,
We'll just have to wait.

Nine, ten,
We're locked out again!

HOUSE

The washing-machine

We're in a fix! We're in a fix!
The washing-machine is up to its tricks.

It's slurping and it's burping,
Spitting water everywhere.
It's sploshing and it's splashing,
Squirting bubbles in the air.

Now it's grinning as it's spinning.
I think I saw it wink.
When they went in, my pants were white.
I bet it's turned them pink!

When it's feeling really naughty,
There's nothing we can do.
It sometimes bites a hole in them
And makes them smaller too!

We're in a fix! We're in a fix!
The washing-machine is up to its tricks.

Blowing bubbles

Hubble, bubble,
Blowing bubbles
On a windy day.

Hubble, bubble,
Watch the bubbles
As they float away.

The Hoover

The Hoover eats up anything—
Crisp crumbs, sweet wrappers, bits of string.

It grubs around behind the door,
Then snakes its way across the floor,

Gobbling up whatever's there—
Paper scraps, dust specks, strands of hair.

Beneath the table, under the chairs,
Along the hallway, up the stairs,

It swallows everything it can,
Like missing bits of Action Man!

Down the landing the Hoover crawls,
Sucking up dust beside the walls.

Crisp crumbs, sweet wrappers, bits of string—
The Hoover eats up anything.

Quick! Hurry up! Tidy the floor.
The Hoover's at your bedroom door!

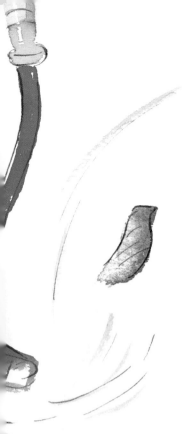

In bed again

One, two, three, four
Lost my temper
Slammed the door.

Five, six, seven, eight
Licked the gravy
From my plate.

Nine, ten
In bed again!

Zoo dream

I dreamed I went to the zoo one day,
All the animals came out to play.
There were:

Ten whales whistling,
Nine hippos hopping,
Eight monkeys marching,
Seven lions laughing,
Six snakes skipping,
Five donkeys dancing,
Four crocodiles clapping,
Three rhinos roaring,
Two giraffes giggling
And one seal snoring!

In the middle of the night

In the middle of the night
When you are sleeping,
Who comes creeping?
Who comes peeping?

Mouse comes creeping.
Mouse comes peeping.
Cat comes creeping.
Cat comes peeping.

In the middle of the night
When you are sleeping,
Who comes creeping?
Who comes peeping?

Mum comes creeping.
Mum comes peeping.
Shoos away the mouse.
Shoos away the cat.
Tucks you in
And leaves you sleeping,
Soundly
      soundly
         soundly
     sleeping.

Snowflakes

Snowflakes are falling,
Falling, falling,
Snowflakes are falling
All over town.
Snowflakes are falling,
Falling, falling,
Wrapping the world
In a bright white gown.

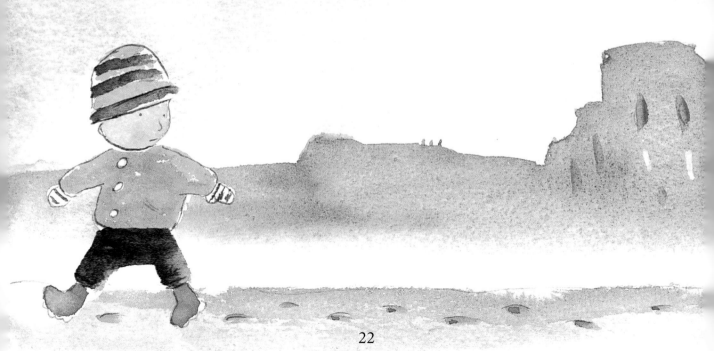

Stamping footprints on a snowy day

Stamping footprints on a snowy day.
One stamp, two stamp.
I stamp, you stamp
On a snowy day.

Stamping footprints on a snowy day.
Three stamp, four stamp.
My stamp, your stamp
On a snowy day.

Stamping footprints on a snowy day.
Five stamp, six stamp.
Flick stamp, kick stamp
On a snowy day.

Stamping footprints on a snowy day.
Seven stamp, eight stamp.
Small stamp, great stamp
On a snowy day.

Stamping footprints on a snowy day.
Nine stamp, ten stamp.
Let's do it again stamp
On a snowy day.

Giant Griff

Giant Griff
Sits on the cliff
With his legs dangling over the side.

The children stand
In a queue on the sand
To use his big toe as a slide.

The sea

The sea can be angry.
The sea can be rough.
The sea can be vicious.
The sea can be tough.

The sea can rip.
The sea can tear.
The sea can roar
Like a hungry bear.

The sea can be gentle.
The sea can be flat.
The sea can be calm
As a sleeping cat.

The sea can glide
Over the sand
Stroking the beach
Like a giant hand.

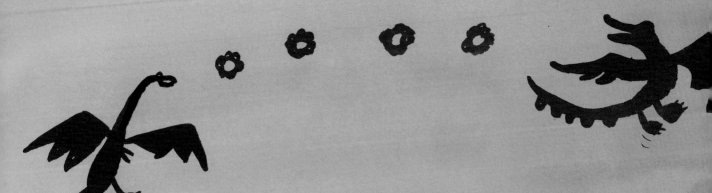

Ten naughty dragons

Ten naughty dragons blowing smoke-rings in a line,
One set himself on fire, then there were nine.

Nine naughty dragons swinging on a gate,
One got her tail trapped, then there were eight.

Eight naughty dragons zooming round the heavens,
One ran out of petrol, then there were seven.

Seven naughty dragons playing silly tricks,
One fell down a well, then there were six.

Six naughty dragons chasing round a hive,
One got stung on her thumb, then there were five.

Five naughty dragons knocked on a castle door,
One was captured by a knight, then there were
   four.

Four naughty dragons splashing in the sea,
One put his fire out, then there were three.

Three naughty dragons at a barbecue,
One fell in an ice bucket, then there were two.

Two naughty dragons flew too near the sun,
One burnt his scales off, then there was one.

One naughty dragon flew off in a rage,
Got caught by a zookeeper and locked in a cage!

Chinese New Year Dragon

There's a brightly coloured dragon
Swaying down the street,
Stomping and stamping
And kicking up its feet.

There's a multi-coloured dragon
—Green, gold, and red—
Twisting and twirling
And shaking its head.

There's a silky-scaled dragon
Parading through the town,
Swishing and swooshing
And rippling up and down.

There's a swirling, whirling dragon,
Weaving to and fro,
Prancing and dancing
And putting on a show.

There's cheering and clapping
As the dragon draws near—
A sign of good luck
And a happy New Year!

28

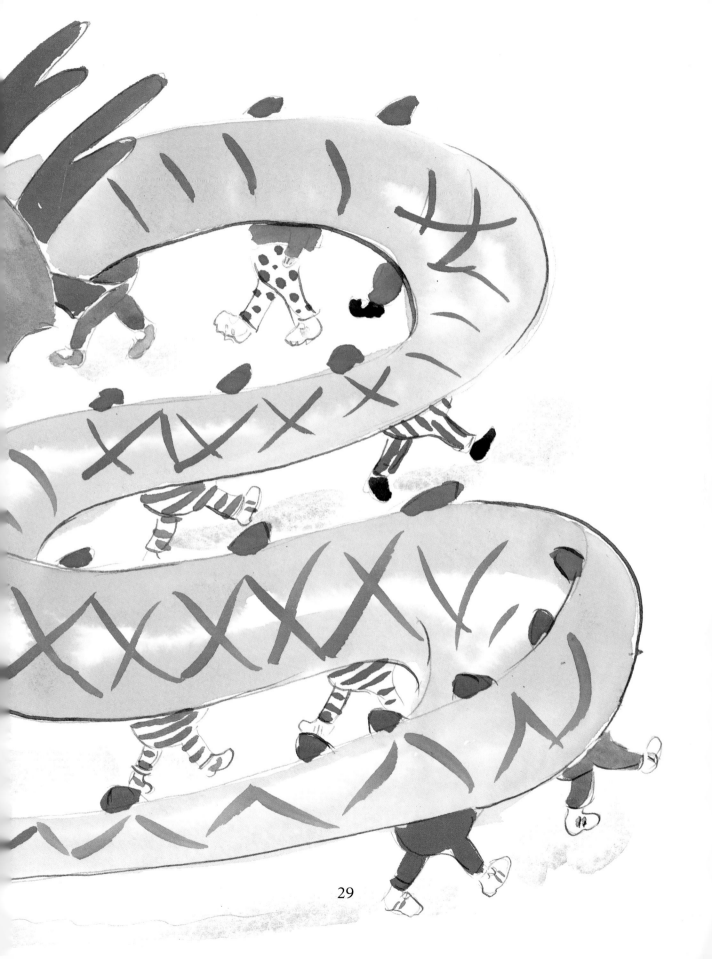

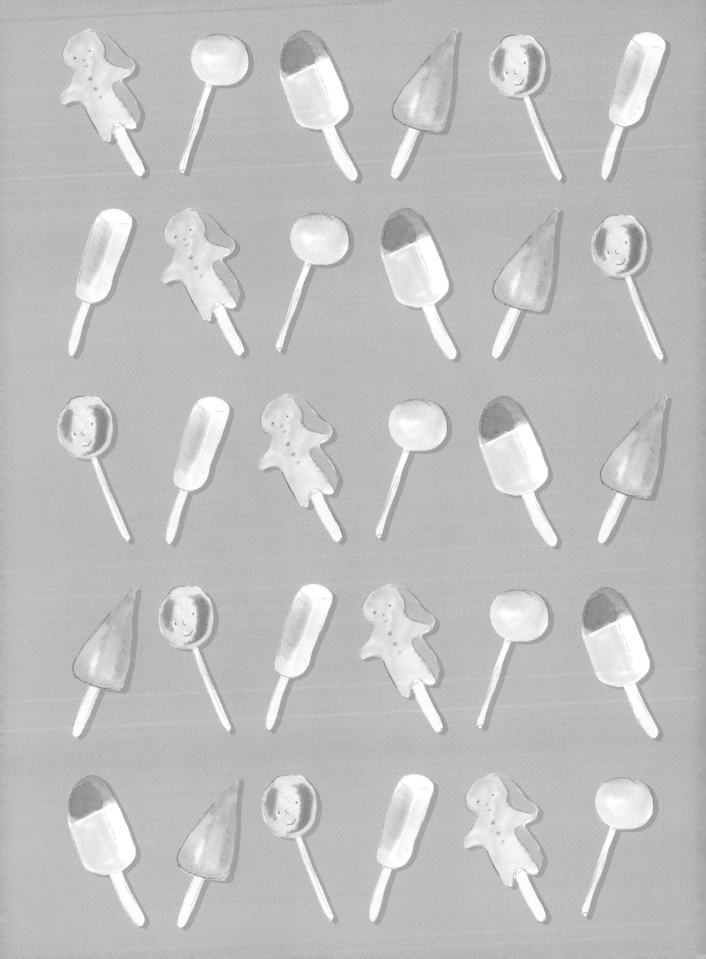

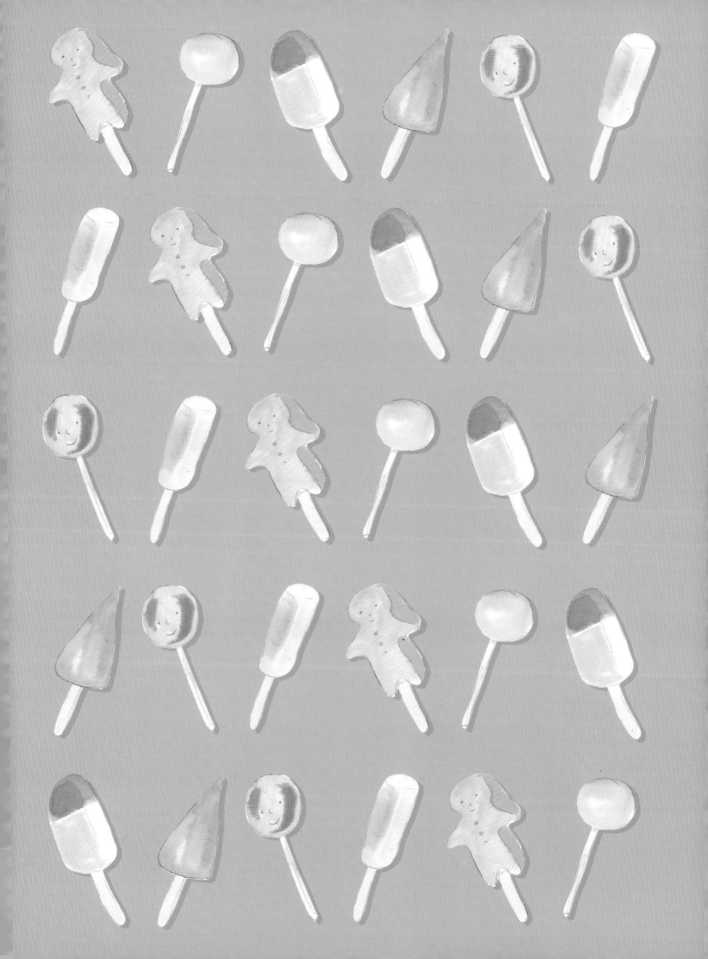